P is for PURPOSE.

Alphabet Affirmations
&
Everything Else You Need to Know Before Kindergarten Activity Book

Written by: J. Lavone Roberson, M.Ed., ECEC

Illustrated by: Senetha Fuller

Dedication

To God. Jehovah Rapha. My healer. Jehovah Shalom. My peace.

To my grandfather's Robert Lee Cobb, Sr. and Joseph "Gompa" Roberson. I felt your presence on every page I wrote in this book. Both of you were unable to be formally educated due to systemic oppression and racism. I do not take for granted the opportunities that have been given to me as a result of your sacrifices and prayers. I am honored that I now get to be an educator in the communities where you worked so hard. I hope I am making you proud. I know you are both watching over me and guiding me from heaven. Rest in love. -Your Granddaughter Lavone

Copyright

Contact Us:

Library of Congress: 2021917393
ISBN: 978-1-7365371-7-6 (Paperback)
Also Available as an E-Book
Printed in USA.
10 9 8 7 6 5 4 3 2
First Edition
August 2021

Author's Message

Dear Reader,

Thank you for choosing this book to help your young learner. I wrote this book because I was a classroom teacher for many years, and know how important it is for students to master core concepts. I always told families that one of the most important things they can do for their child is READ TO THEM. I believe this wholeheartedly, which is one of the reasons I also became an author. I wanted to create learning materials that families and educators could use to help children to learn. Each book has tips and tools to help the adults learn ways to support their young learner.

The theme of this book, and every book I've written, is purpose. Purpose helps us to answer the question WHY. The reason why this book is important is because mastery of these core foundational skills prepares students for future reading, writing, math, and more.

This book is FULL of activities, tips, and resources to help you, and the children you share it with, learn. There is so much to share so throughout this book you will see QR codes that lead you to additional resources; i.e. videos, books, websites, etc. Please share your completion certificates @nowiamniabooks or www.nowiamnia.org , you could win a prize!

My mom Jackie Roberson always shares that Malcolm X once said *"Education is the passport for our future, for tomorrow belongs to those who prepare for it today."* I hope this book helps you and your young learner to be better prepared for school and beyond.

Happy Reading!

With Love,

Meet The Author & Illustrator

Jacquelyn "Lavone" Roberson is an author, educator, and philanthropist from Connecticut. Lavone is the CEO and Founder of The Now I Am Nia Foundation, Inc., where she leads various projects to support communities in need. Lavone is an alumni of Hampton University and a member of Delta Sigma Theta Sorority, Incorporated. She has a B.S. in Sociology, a Master's in Elementary Education,

and an ABD Doctorate in Educational Leadership. As a teacher she was selected to be in the nation's first Quad-D lab classroom cohort. When she is not teaching or working in the community, she enjoys spending time with her family, god children, and MaltiPoo Worthy. To learn more please visit www.NowIAmNia.org and follow us @NowIAmNiaBooks. 1 Corinthians 10:31

Senetha Fuller resides in Philadelphia, PA. She specializes in "urban art" but can create custom art using different mediums. It has always been her passion to inspire through her art. @Red_Panda_Artz

Table of Contents

Alphabet Affirmations

Social Emotional Learning:

<u>5 Ways to improve a child's self-esteem:</u>

1. **Be consistent.** Consistency and routines help to build trust.
2. **Ask their input.** Children know very early on how they feel, what they like, and what they dislike.
3. **Allow them to help** and reward their efforts with positive praise.
4. **Compliment them and affirm them.** Let them know how AMAZING they are and how proud you are of them.
5. **Create new experiences together.** Field trips, adventures, crafts, cooking together, etc... are great ways to bond and create memories as a family.

"With confidence, you have won before you have started."
-Marcus Garvey

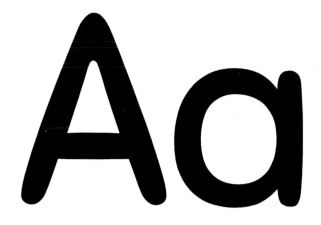

Aa

I am AMAZING.

I am APPRECIATIVE.

I am AWESOME.

I am AMBITIOUS.

I am ALIVE.

I am ADORED.

I am ARTISTIC.

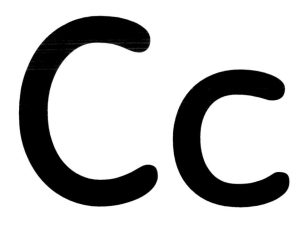

Cc

I am COURAGEOUS.

I am CARING.

I am CAREFUL.

I am COOL.

I am CREATIVE.

I am CONFIDENT.

Dd

I am DIFFERENT.

I am DARING.

I am DYNAMIC.

I am DIVINE.

I am DELIGHTFUL.

Ee

I am EVOLVING.

I am EQUAL.

I am ENOUGH.

I am EMPOWERED.

I am EXCITED.

I am ENTHUSIASTIC.

I am ENLIGHTENED

I am EMPOWERED.

E is for EATING. Yum!

Ff

I am FREE.

I am FUN.

I am FRIENDLY.

I am FOCUSED.

F is for fishing!

Ii

I am INTELLIGENT.
I am INCLUSIVE.
I am INSPIRING.

Jj

I am JOYFUL.

I am a JOKING.
I am JOLLY.

Kk

I am KIND.
I am KNOWLEDGEABLE.

Ll

I am LOVED.
I am LOVEABLE.
I am LOVING.
I am LOVE.
I am LOYAL.
I am LEARNING.
I am LISTENING.
I am LIVING.

Mm

I am MAGICAL.
I am MOTIVATED.
I am MIRACULOUS.
I am MAGNIFICENT.
I am ME.

Nn

I am NICE.
I am NOBLE.
I am NOTICED.
I am NOTORIOUS.

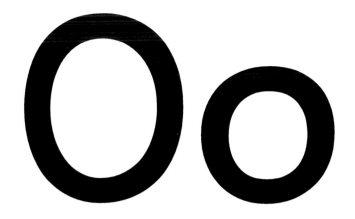

Oo

I am **OUTSTANDING.**
I am OPTIMISTIC.
I am **OKAY.**

Pp

I am PATIENT.
I am POSITIVE.
I am PASSIONATE.
I am PEACEFUL.

I am PLAYFUL.
I am PRECIOUS.
I am POWERFUL.
I am PROUD.

I have PURPOSE.

Scan for more info.

Qq

I am QUIET.
I am QUALITY.
I am QUALIFIED.

Rr

I am ROYALTY.
I am RESPECTFUL.
I am RESOURCEFUL.
I am RADIANT.
I am READY.
I am RECEPTIVE.
I am RELAXED.
I am REFRESHED.
I am RELIEVED.
I am RENEWED.
I am RESILIENT.

Ss

I am SAFE.
I am SMART.
I am SILLY.
I am SPECIAL.
I am SINCERE.
I am SUCCESSFUL.
I am STRONG.
I am SPECTACULAR.
I am SENSATIONAL.

Tt

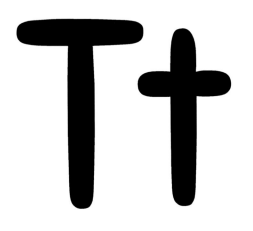

I am TERRIFIC.
I am TRYING.
I am TALENTED.
I am TRUSTWORTHY.
I am THANKFUL.

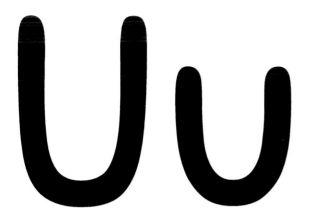

Uu

I am UNIQUE.
I am UNDERSTANDING.
I am UPLIFTING.
I am UNLIMITED.

Vv

I am VICTORIOUS.
I am VALUABLE.
I am VIBRANT.

Ww

I am WISE.
I am WORTHY.
I am WINNING.
I am WHOLE.
I am WONDERFUL.

Xx

I am eXtraordinary!

Yy

I am YOUTHFUL.

Zz

I am ZESTY.
I am Zen.
I am ZANY.

Letters

Learning Skills:

- **Letter recognition** is one of the earliest steps to learning how to read.
  - Sing "The ABC Song" and have children begin recognizing the letters of the alphabet in order and out of order.
- Practice **writing letters** to strengthen fine motor skills.
- **Recognizing words** that begin with each letter and practicing the letter sounds is **phonics**. **Phonics is the relationship between the letter and its sound.**
- **Practice writing your capital and lowercase letters.**
  - Capital letters are usually larger than lowercase letters. They are used for proper nouns; people, places, and things. Sentences also start with capital letters. Your name begins with a capital letter but the rest of your name has lowercase letters.

Scan for videos to help with learning the alphabet.

Capital Letters

ABCDEFG
HIJKLMN
OPQRST
UVWXYZ

Lowercase Letters

abcdefg
hijklmn
opqrstu
vwxyz

Alphabet

Aa	Bb	Cc	Dd	Ee
Ff	Gg	Hh	Ii	Jj
Kk	Ll	Mm	Nn	Oo
Pp	Qq	Rr	Ss	Tt
Uu	Vv	Ww	Xx	Yy
				Zz

Letters **A, E, I, O, U,** and sometimes **Y** are called **VOWELS!**

Sing the alphabet song...

ant

ackee

apple

acorn

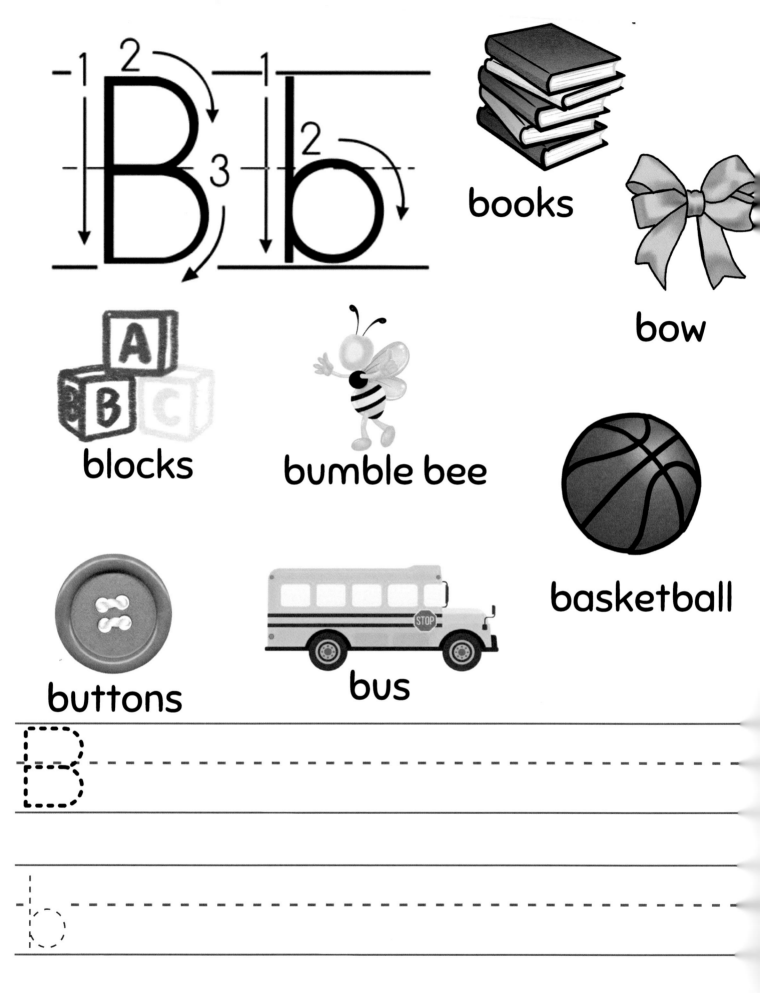

books

bow

blocks

bumble bee

basketball

buttons

bus

Bb

C C

candy

cupcake

clouds

candy corn

donkey

dinosaur

dress

aonuτ

Dd

elephant

envelope

eggs

eyes

Ee

Name: _____

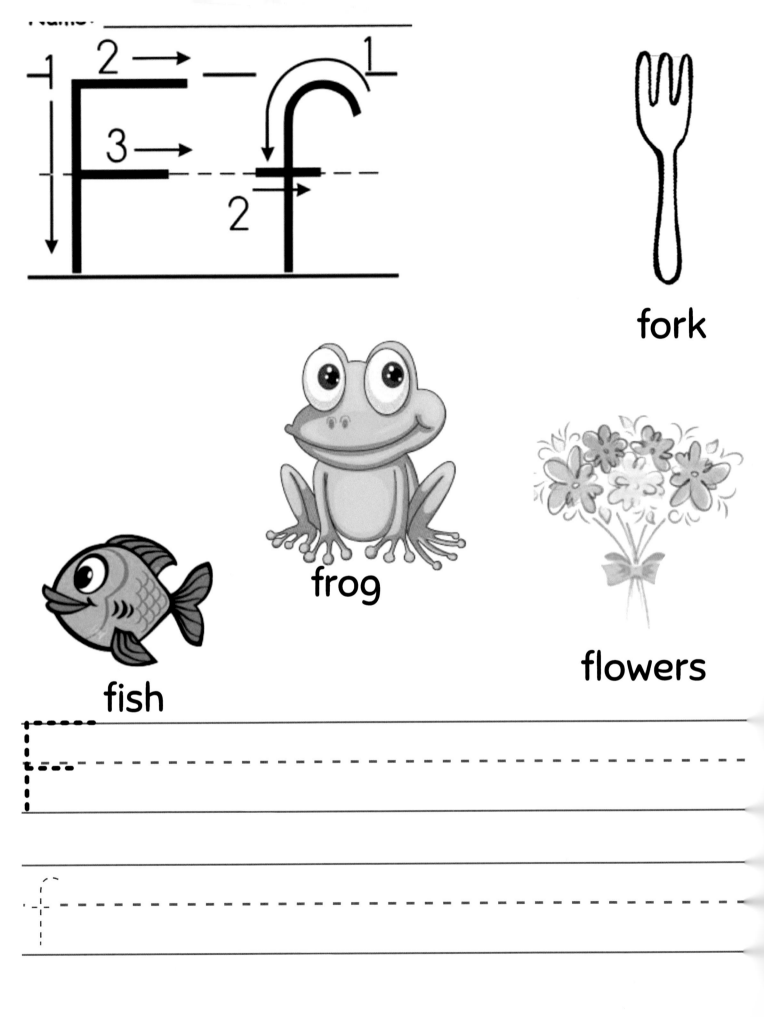

fork

frog

fish

flowers

grapes

gloves

glasses

goat

guitar

Gg

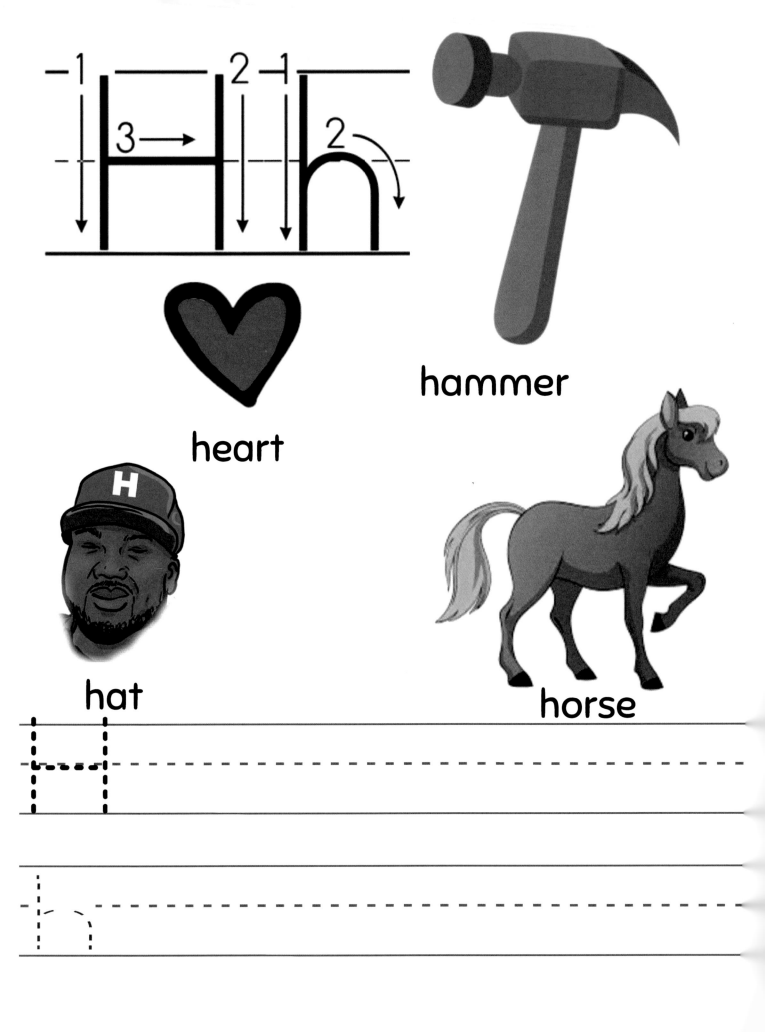

heart

hammer

hat

horse

Hh

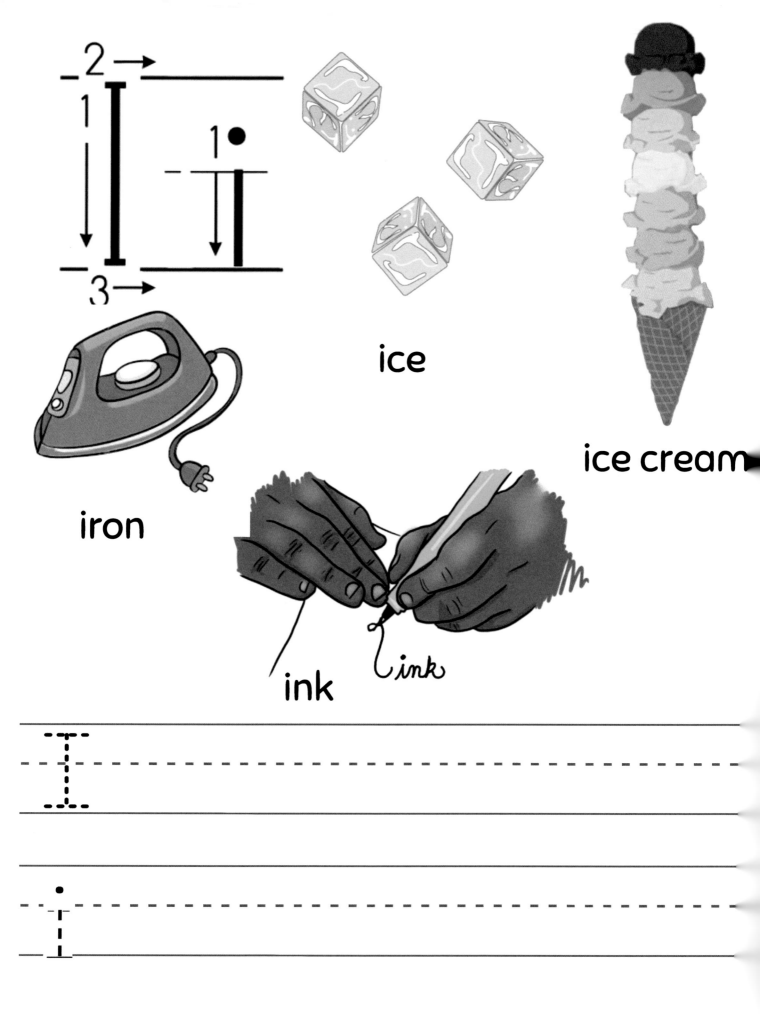

ice

ice cream

iron

ink

 Ii

jumping rope

juicebox

juice

jellyfish

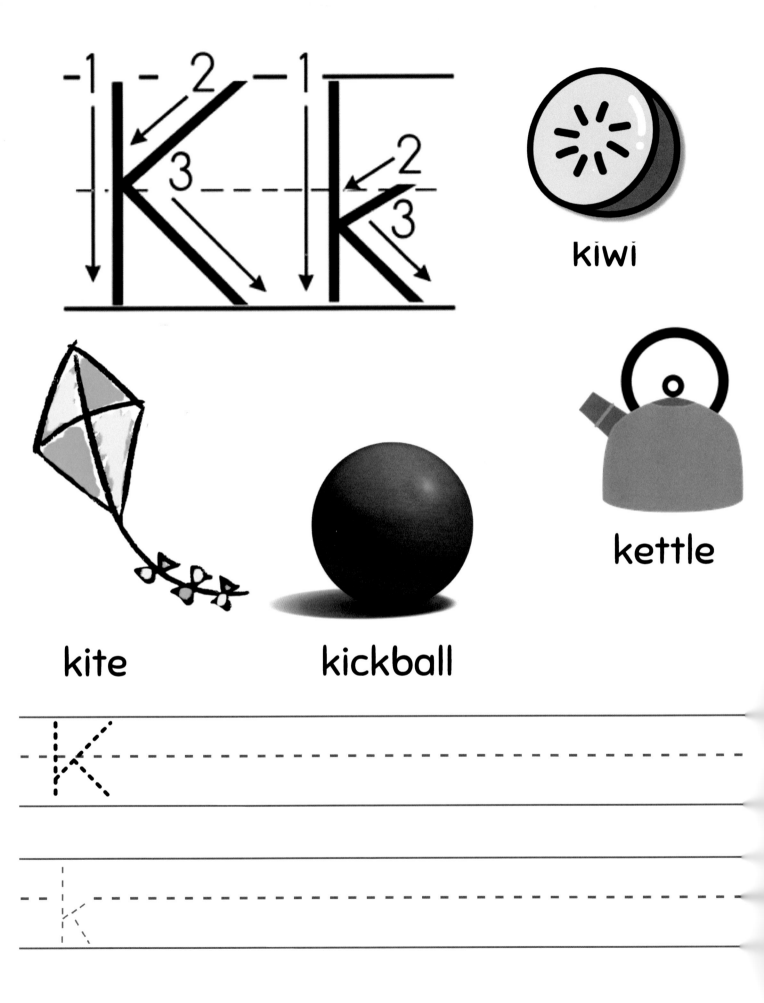

kiwi

kite

kickball

kettle

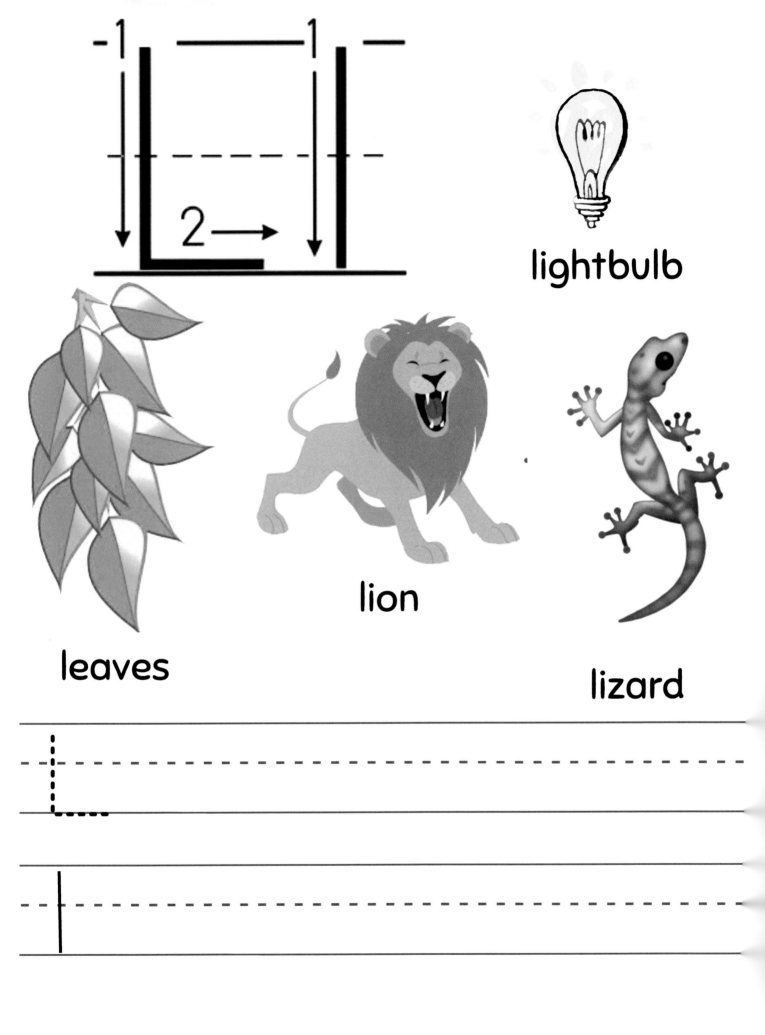

leaves

lion

lightbulb

lizard

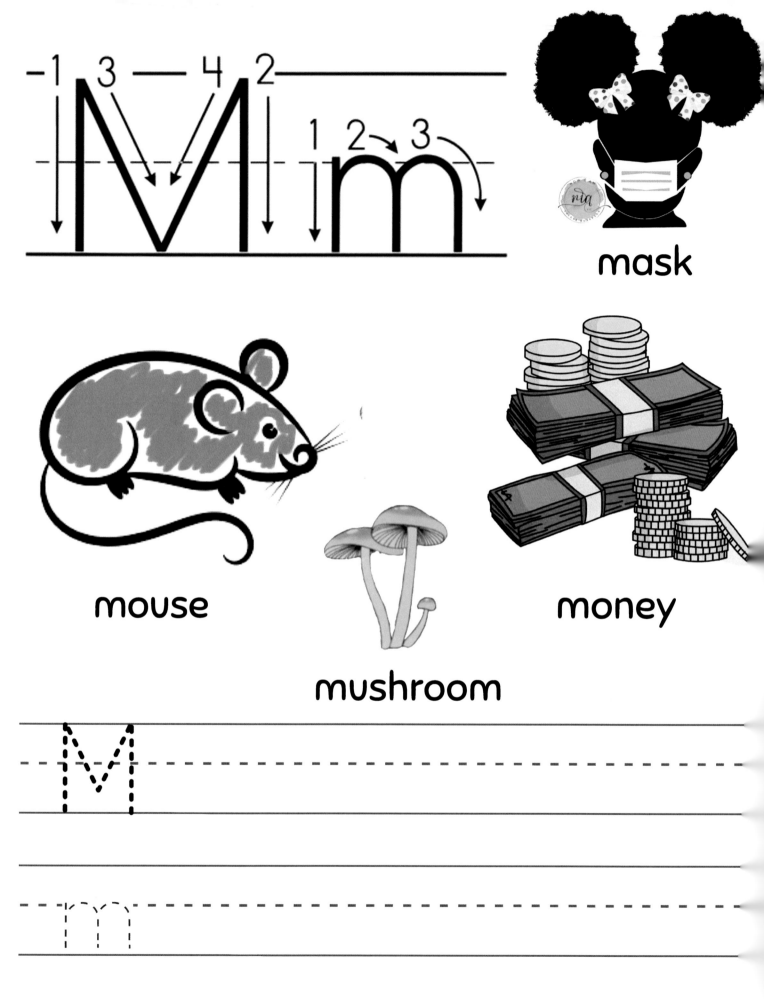

mask

mouse

mushroom

money

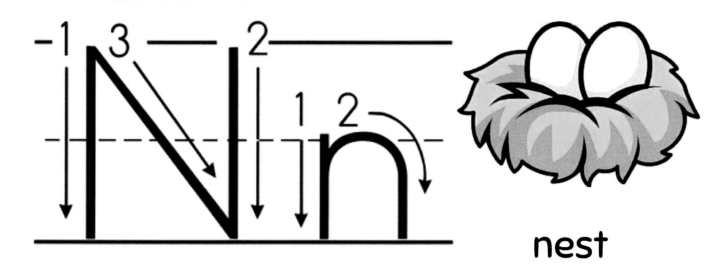

nest

nails

notebook

N

n

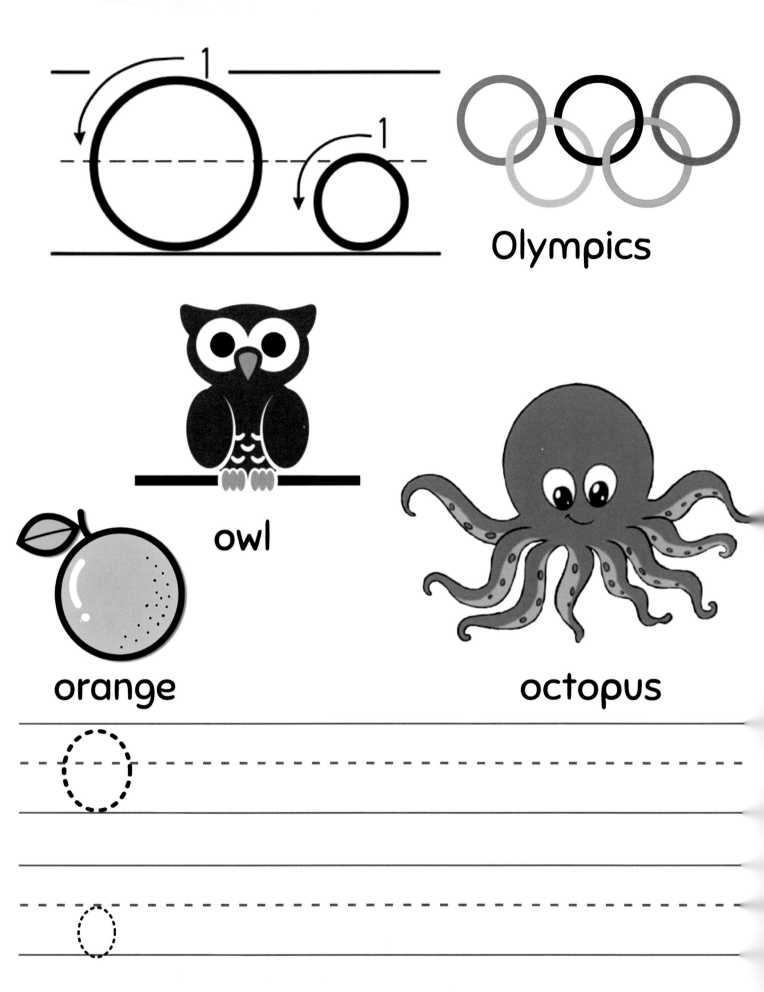

Olympics

owl

orange

octopus

pizza

pencil

pineapple

pig

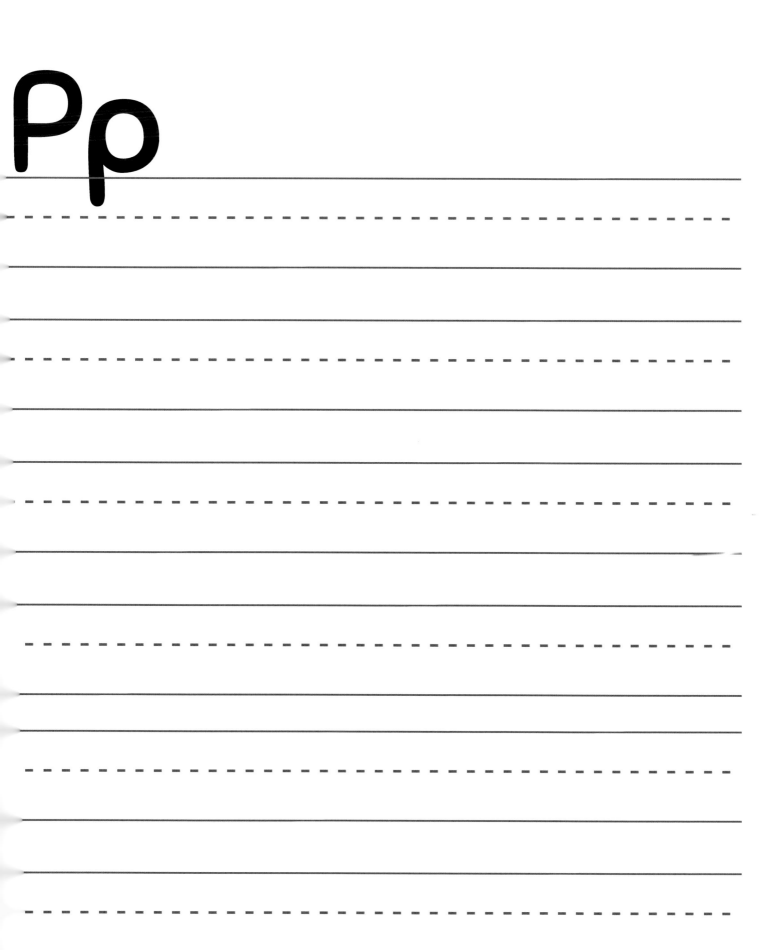

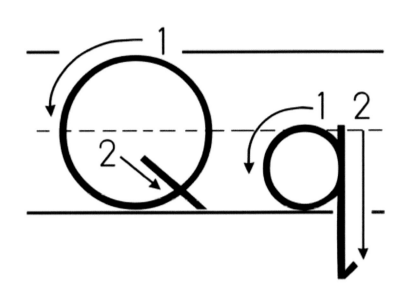

question mark

quilt

Queen

quarter

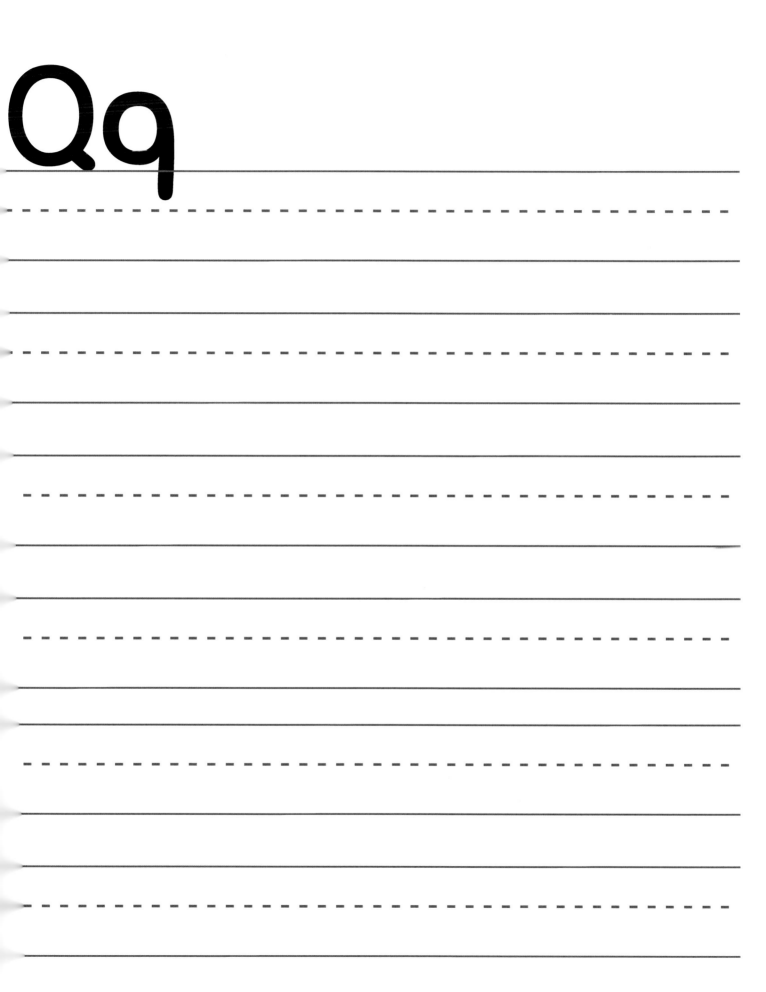

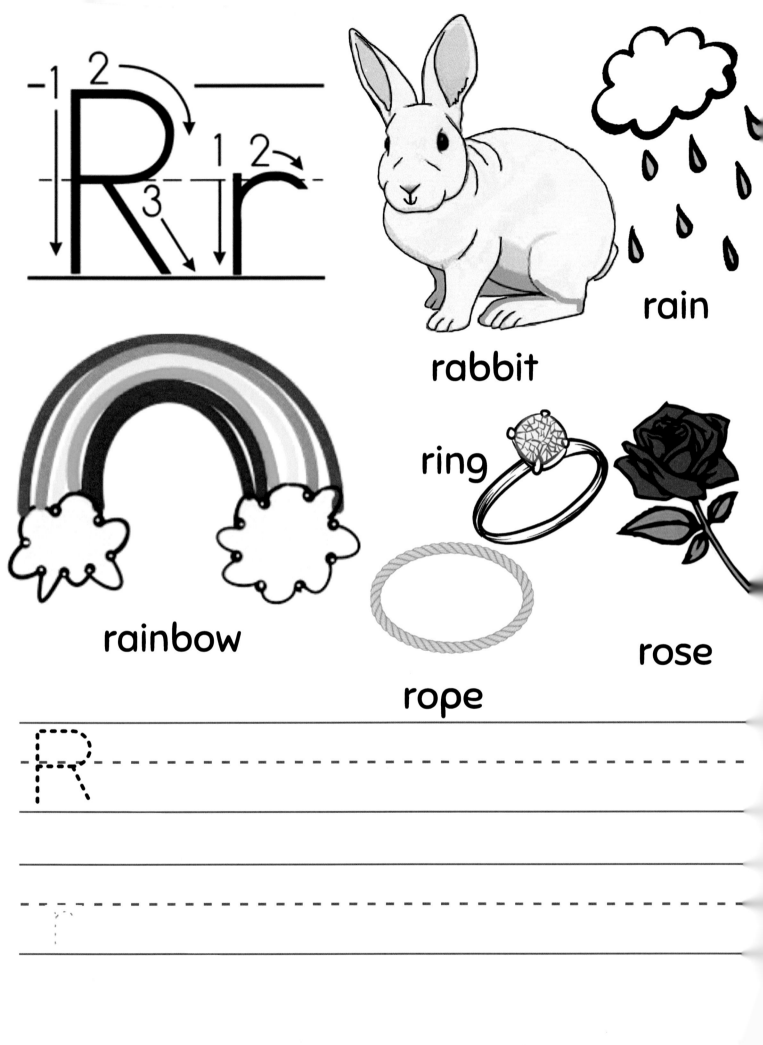

rabbit

rain

rainbow

ring

rope

rose

Rr

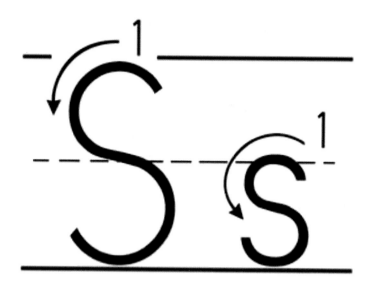

shoes
sneakers

stars

sunglasses

strawberry

socks

Ss

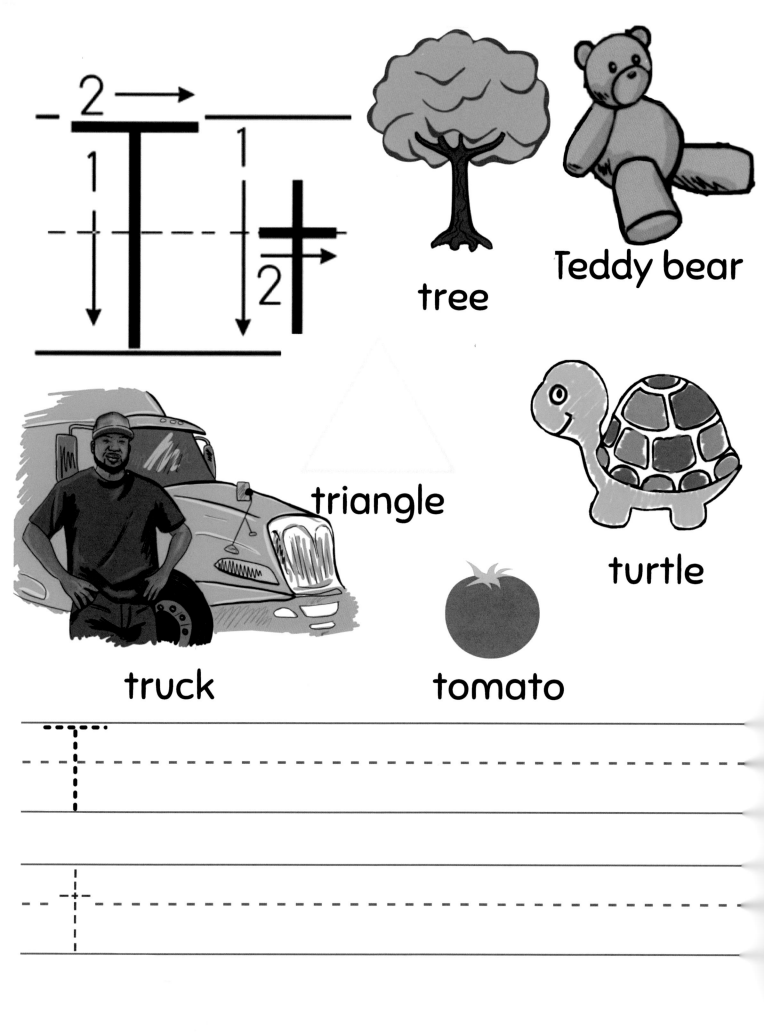

tree

Teddy bear

triangle

turtle

truck

tomato

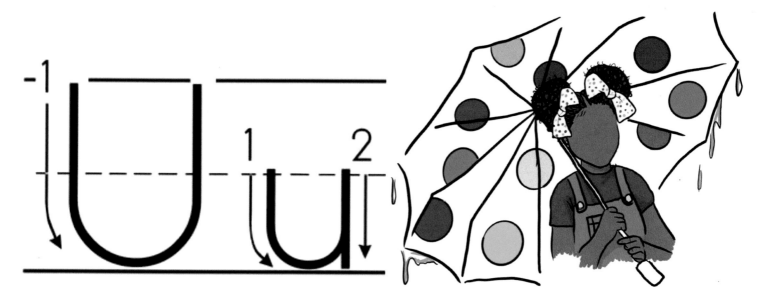

umbrella

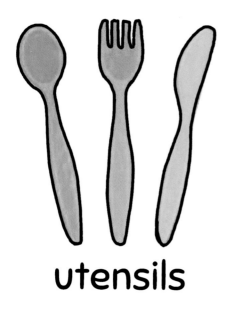

utensils

unicorn

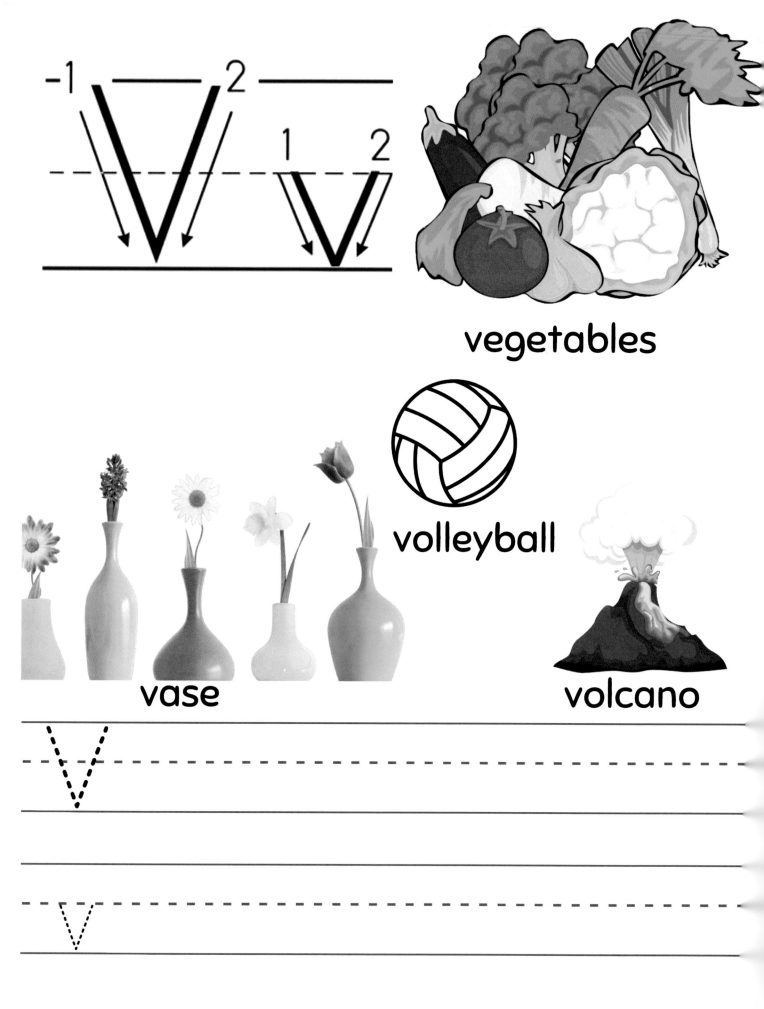

vegetables

volleyball

vase

volcano

Vv

water

watermelon

watch

window

wave

whale

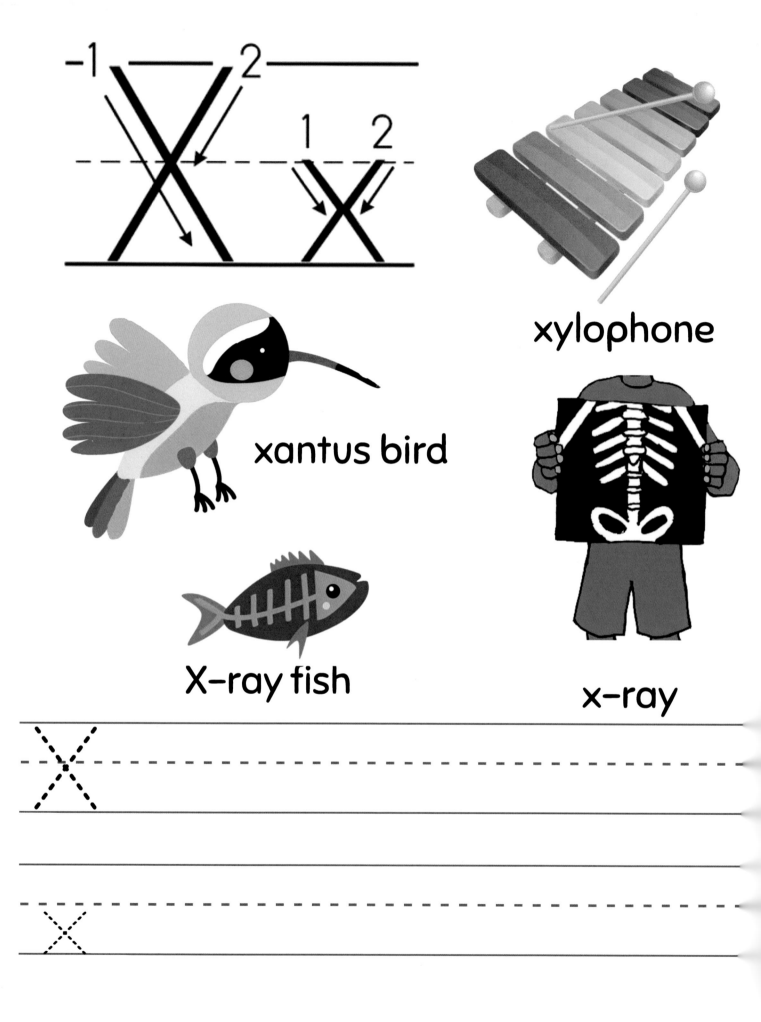

xylophone

xantus bird

X-ray fish

x-ray

Xx

yak

Yellow

Yarn

yo-yo

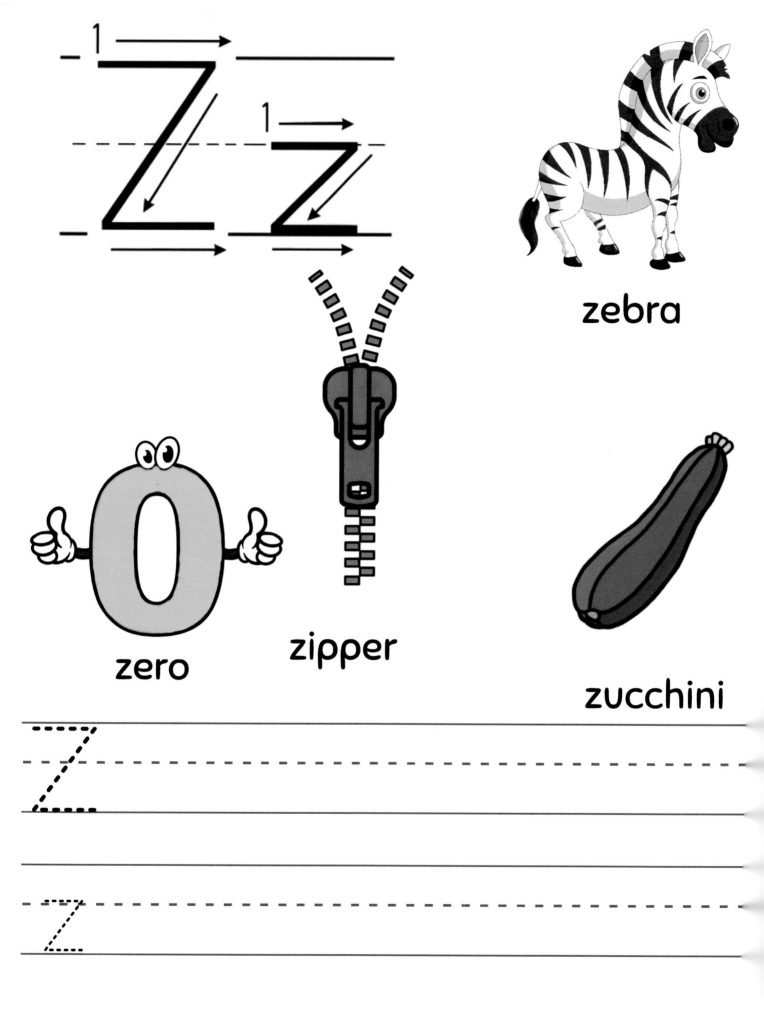

zebra

zero

zipper

zucchini

Alphabet Fill In

Fill in the missing letters to complete the alphabet.

Aa	Bb		Dd	Ee
Ff		Hh		Jj
	Ll	Mm		Oo
Pp		Rr	Ss	Tt
	Vv	Ww		
				Zz

Phonics
Short & Long Vowel Sounds

SHORT vowel sounds: say the letters sound. A is for aaahh-ple (apple).

LONG vowel sounds: say the letter's name. A is for Ayy-corn (acorn).

	SHORT		LONG	
a	apple	ah cat	paper	cake
e	net	eh elephant	leaf	bees
i	pig	ih lizard	ice cream	kite
o	dog	oah octopus	ocean	soap
u	sun	uh umbrella	glue	unicorn

Phonological Awareness

Listening
cat/car
Do these words sound the same?

Blending
c/a/t   cat
Can you blend this word back together?

Read Alouds are great ways to teach these skills.

Alliteration
dog - dinner
Do these words begin with the same sound?

Rhyming
cat/hat
Do these words rhyme?

Segmentation
map m/a/p
Can you break this word apart by sounding it out?

Scan for read alouds.

Syllables
Happy = 2
How many syllables in the word?

NUMBERS

Numbers are EVERYWHERE. Here are some helpful ways to help children learn their numbers.

Look for numbers on household and community signs. i.e. exit signs, mile markers, remote controls, food items, etc.

When walking through the grocery store have children estimate how much items are, or how much the entire total will be.

Count the number of stairs whenever you're walking up or down.

Play counting games online or watch videos that teach counting their favorite things. i.e. counting cars, dolls, paintbrushes.

Make flashcards and use them to count household items such as: How many forks to we have? How many cups do we have? How many doors do we have?

Numbers

									0
1	2	3	4	5	6	7	8	9	10
11	12	13	14	15	16	17	18	19	20
21	22	23	24	25	26	27	28	29	30
31	32	33	34	35	36	37	38	39	40
41	42	43	44	45	46	47	48	49	50
51	52	53	54	55	56	57	58	59	60
61	62	63	64	65	66	67	68	69	70
71	72	73	74	75	76	77	78	79	80
81	82	83	84	85	86	87	88	89	90
91	92	93	94	95	96	97	98	99	100

Count & Trace

Count the numbers.
Notice the pattern.

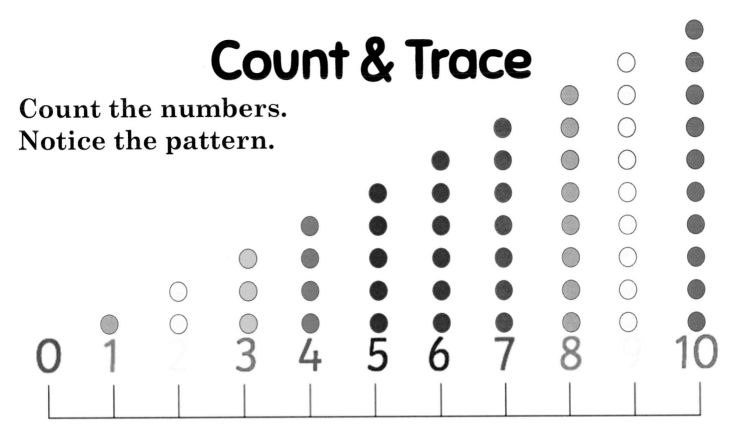

0 1 2 3 4 5 6 7 8 9 10

Trace the numbers.

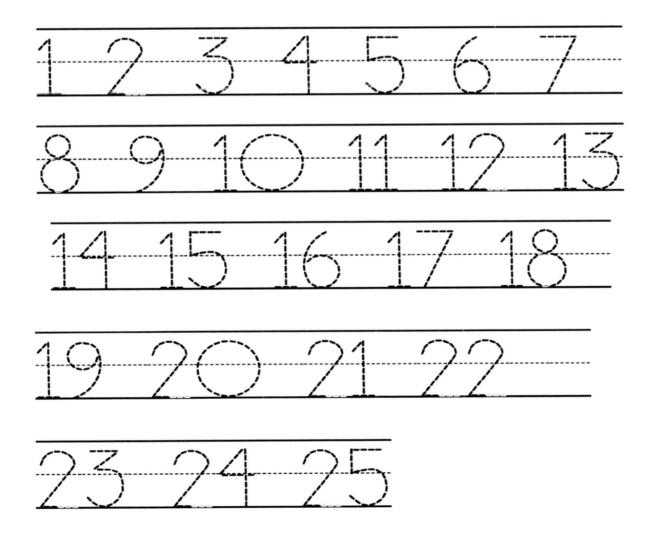

1 2 3 4 5 6 7

8 9 10 11 12 13

14 15 16 17 18

19 20 21 22

23 24 25

Write Numbers

Please use the lines to help you write your numbers.

O

1

2

3

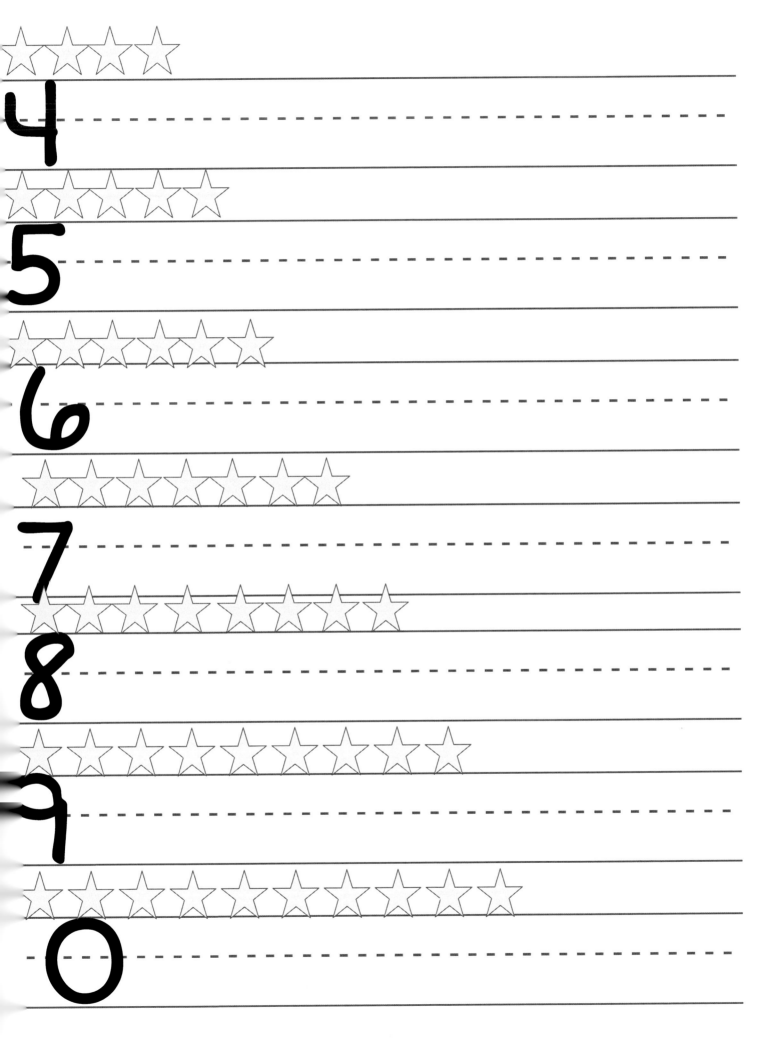

11

12

13

14

15

16

17

18

19

20

Which numbers come next? Write them on the lines below.

Counting

Count each item in each box. Write the number of items on the line.

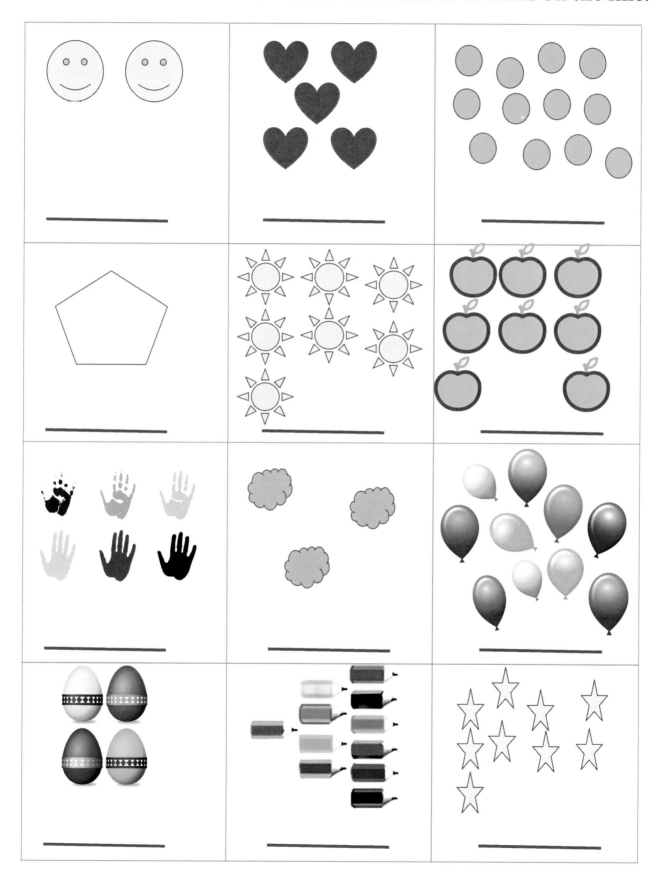

Count & Color

Color in the correct number of circles to match each number.

8	○ ○ ○ ○ ○ ○ ○ ○ ○ ○
6	○ ○ ○ ○ ○ ○ ○ ○ ○ ○
1	○ ○ ○ ○ ○ ○ ○ ○ ○ ○
7	○ ○ ○ ○ ○ ○ ○ ○ ○ ○
10	○ ○ ○ ○ ○ ○ ○ ○ ○ ○
4	○ ○ ○ ○ ○ ○ ○ ○ ○ ○
2	○ ○ ○ ○ ○ ○ ○ ○ ○ ○
5	○ ○ ○ ○ ○ ○ ○ ○ ○ ○
9	○ ○ ○ ○ ○ ○ ○ ○ ○ ○
3	○ ○ ○ ○ ○ ○ ○ ○ ○ ○

Mystery Numbers

Write the missing numbers.

1	2		4	
6			9	10
	12	13	14	
16		18		20
21	22			25

SHAPES

I am a **triangle**.
What else would I be?
Everywhere I go people recognize me.
I am cool because I have **always 3 sides**.
I can be acute, obtuse, or right angled... whatever I decide.

I am a **square**.
Everyone knows me.
I have **4 sides** so what else could I be?
All of my sides are equal.
That makes me feel great.
I also forgot to mention, my **sides are always straight**.

I am a **rectangle**.
I have **4 sides** too.
There are some special things about me ... let me name a few.
My sides are all stretched out but the **opposite sides are the same**.
People confuse me with a square but don't forget my name.

I am a **circle**.
What else could I be?
Nothing else goes round and round faster than me.
I am very smart.
Everytime I go around, I end up where I start.

I am a **star**.
When you see me stop and stare.
If you **look up in the sky at night**, you'll usually see me there.

Shapes are cool and fun to learn, you'll see them everywhere.
You'll see the shapes in your home, up here, and over there.

By: J. Lavone Roberson and Braylynn Mae Smith

square

I have...

- 4 sides.
- Straight Lines.
- 4 equal sides.
- Opposite sides parallel.

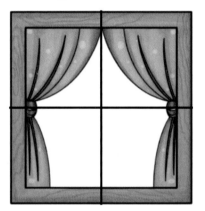

Use this space to draw squares:

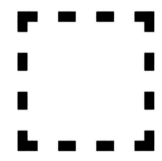

circle

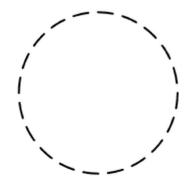

I have...
- Round shape.
- No sides.
- No lines.

Use this space to draw circles:

triangle

I have...

- 3 sides.
- Straight lines.

Use this space to draw triangles:

rectangle

I have...
- 4 sides.
- 4 corners.
- Opposite sides parallel.
- Opposite sides the same length.

Use this space to draw rectangles:

heart

The heart shape is usually used to show love.

Use this space to draw hearts:

star

I am a...
- Closed shape.
- Straight lines.
- Regular polygon.

Use this space to draw stars:

diamond

I am a...
- 2-dimensional flat shape.
- Straight lines.
- Regular polygon.
- Closed shape.
- Also called a rhombus.
- Also called a parallelogram.

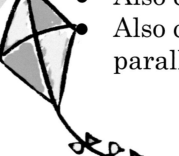

Use this space to draw diamonds:

oval

I have ...
- A round body but I am not a circle.
- No lines or sides.

Use this space to draw ovals:

pentagon

I have...

- 5 sides.
- A 2-dimensional flat shape.
- Straight lines.
- A closed shape.

Use this space to draw pentagons:

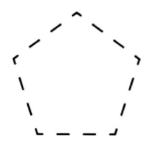

hexagon

I have...

- 6 sides.
- A 2-dimensional flat shape.
- Straight lines.
- A closed shape.

Use this space to draw hexagons:

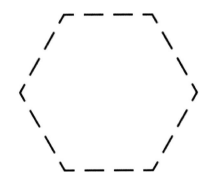

octagon

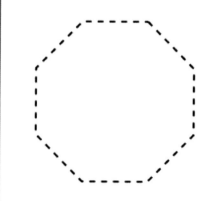

I have...

- 8 sides.
- A 2-dimensional flat shape.
- Straight lines.
- A closed shape.

Use this space to draw octagons:

Matching Shapes

Match the shape with its name.

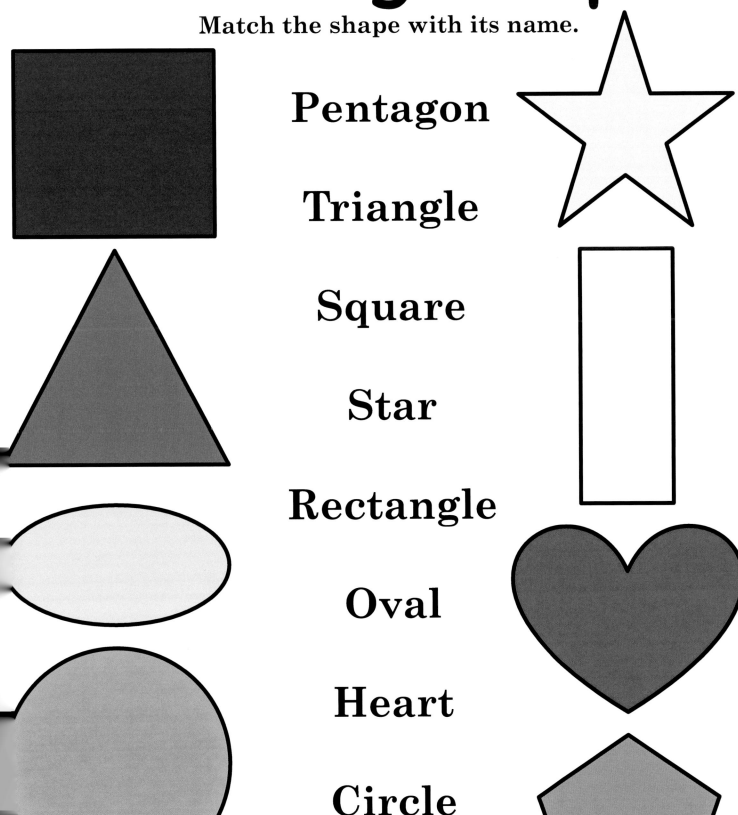

Pentagon

Triangle

Square

Star

Rectangle

Oval

Heart

Circle

Shapes All Around

Find items in your home that are different shapes. Write down what you found. Which shape has the most items in your home?

Shape	Things I Found
●	
■	
▲	
▬	
◆	
♥	
★	

COLORS

Teaching colors is an act of practice and repetition. Share the colors of everyday items to help children associate the color with its name.

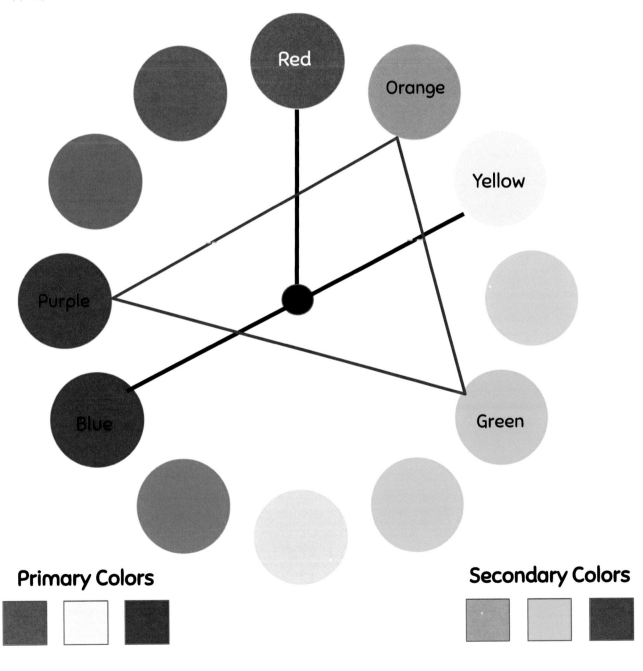

Primary Colors

Secondary Colors

red

Use a red crayon. Draw something red.

orange

Use an orange crayon. Draw something orange.

yellow

Use a yellow crayon. Draw something yellow.

green

Use a green crayon. Draw something green.

blue

Use a blue crayon. Draw something blue.

purple

Use a purple crayon. Draw something purple.

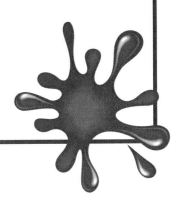

pink

Use a pink crayon. Draw something pink.

black

se a black crayon. Draw something black.

white

Use a white crayon. Draw something white.

brown

Use a brown crayon. Draw something brown.

◉◉I Spy Colors

Find things around you that are in each color. Draw a picture of that item

Red	Orange	Yellow
Green	Blue	Purple
Pink	Brown	Black

CIRCLE TIME LEARNING

Circle time is used to reinforce primary learning skills and to build positive relationships with children.

Learning happens everywhere.

Here are some things you can do during learning time with children.

Ask children to talk about themselves. *What are your favorite....*

Practice Transitions

Dance Party

Ask children about their favorite people. *Who is your best friend? Why?*

Ask children about their feelings. *What makes you happy? What makes you sad?*

Show & Tell

Ask children about their needs. *What can I help you with?*

Ask children to share a story. *Tell me about a time when...*

Read Alouds

Sing Alongs

Quiet Time

Create Flash Cards

Please write your name.

with a pencil

with a crayon

with a marker

in different colors

My First Name

My first name is

I have _____ letters in my first name.

Draw a picture of something that begins with the same letter as your first name.

What does your name mean?

Hi.
My name is Nia.
Nia means purpose.
Scan for more info...

All about me...

My name is...

I am _____ years old.

My birthday is:

_____

My address:

My phone number:

A picture of me:

My favorites:

Color:

Food:

Color in the days of the week.

MONTHS of the YEAR

January
February
March
April
May
June
July
August
September
October
November
December

Put a check next to the spring months.

Circle your birthday month.

Put a star next to black history month.

Cross out the winter months.

Learn the Months of the Year

April	Monday	January	October
Wednesday	March	May	February
December	Saturday	June	August
July	September	Thursday	November

Color the months blue. Color the days red. Write the months in order on the lines below.

1. _____

2. _____

3. _____

4. _____

5. _____

6. _____

7. _____

8. _____

9. _____

10. _____

11. _____

12. _____

The 4 Seasons

Winter	Spring
December, January, February, March	April, May
Summer	Fall
June, July, August	September, October, November

Read Alouds
Curated to celebrate diverse children's books.

Black Lead Characters

- "Nia Means Purpose: The Learner's Edition" by J. Lavone Roberson (available in Spanish)*
- "Nia and The Polka Dot Blanket Project" by J.Lavone Roberson*
- "Everybody Needs Courage" by Senetha Fuller and J. Lavone Roberson*
- "Grandfather's Garden" by Ny-Aja Boyd*
- "Hair Love" By Matthew Cherry*
- "Missing Daddy" by Mariame Kaba*
- "All Because You Matter" by Tami Charles*
- "I Am Every Good Thing" by Derrick Barnes and Gordon C. James*
- "I Am a Phenomenal Black Boy" by Franceca Andre*
- "I Promise" by LeBron James*
- "Brown Boy Joy" by Dr. Thomishia Booker
- "Hair Like Mine" LaTashia Perry*
- "Skin Like Mine" by LaTashia Perry
- "Last Stop on Market Street" by Matt de la Pena
- "The Oldest Student" by Rita Lorraine Hubbard
- "I Am Enough" by Grace Byers
- "You Matter" by Christian
- "The Day You Begin" Jacqueline Woodson*
- "Last Stop on Market Street" by Matt de la Pena
- "Each Kindness" Jacqueline Woodson*
- "Across The Alley" by Richard Michelson
- "Visiting Day" by Jacqueline Woodson

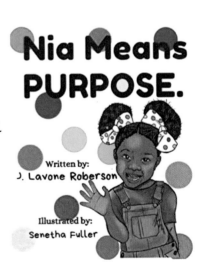

Hispanic & Latinx Lead Characters

- "Nia Significa Proposito: La Educación Educacional en Espanol" by J. Lavone Roberson, Translated by Andrea Cantos*
- "Alma and How She Got Her Name" by Jiana Martinez-Neal*
- "Mama's Nightingale: A Story of Immigration and Separation" by Edwidge Danticat*
- "My Papi Has a Motorcycle" by Isabel Quintero*
- "A Different Pond" by Bao Phi*
- "Dreamers" by Yuyi Morales*
- "Separate is Never Equal: Sylvia Mendez & Her Family's Fight for Desegregation" by Duncan Tonatiuh *

Indigineous Native American Lead Characters

- "We Are Grateful" Traci Sorell *
- "We Are Water Protectors" by Carole Lindstrom*
- "When We Were Alone" by David Robertson*
- "Fry Bread: A Native American Family Story" by Kevin Noble Maillard*

Culture, Historical Events, & Religion

- "The Prodest Blue: The Story of Hijab and Family" by Ibtihaj Muhammad*
- "Lailah's Lunchbox: A Ramadan Story" by Reem Faruqi*
- "Same, Same but Different" by Jenny Sue Kostecki-Shaw*
- "The Whispering Town" by Jennifer Elvgren*
- "The Story of the Underground Railroad" by Conrad Stein
- "What if God was in My Pocket" By Ayonna Johnson
- "Everybody Cooks Rice" Norah Dooley
- "Ben and the Emancipation Proclamation" by Pat Sherman*

Other DEI Books:

- "Harbor Me" by Jacqueline Woodson*
- "The New Kid" by Jerry Craft*
- "Defeated" by James Voytek *
- "All Are Welcome" Alexandra Penfold*
- "Eraser" by Anna Kang
- "You Matter" by Christian Robinson

LGBTQIA+

- "Red: A Crayon's Story" by Michael Hall

Sight Words

the	he	at	but	there
of	was	be	not	use
and	for	this	what	an
a	on	have	all	each
to	are	from	were	which
in	as	or	we	she
is	with	one	when	do
you	his	had	your	how
that	they	by	can	their
it	I	words	said	if

will	some	two	my	find
up	her	more	than	long
other	would	write	first	down
about	make	go	water	day
out	like	see	been	did
many	him	number	call	get
then	into	no	who	come
them	time	way	am	made
these	has	could	its	may
so	look	people	now	part

September

the	to
and	a
I	you
it	in
said	for
up	look
is	red

October

go	we
little	down
can	see
not	one
my	me
big	come
where	orange

November

jump	away
here	help
make	two
play	run
find	three
funny	he
was	yellow

December

that	she
on	they
but	at
with	all
there	out
be	have
am	green

January

do	did
what	so
get	like
this	will
yes	went
are	now
no	blue

February

came	ride
into	good
want	too
pretty	four
saw	well
ran	eat
who	purple

March

new	must
soon	our
ate	say
under	please
of	his
had	him
her	pink

April

some	as
then	could
when	were
them	ask
an	over
just	from
black	white

May

any	how
know	put
take	every
old	by
after	think
let	going
walk	brown

Dolch Sight Words

a	am	are	ate	
be	black	brown	but	came
did	do	eat	four	get
good	have	he	into	like
must	new	now	on	
our	out	please	pretty	ran
ride	saw	say	she	so
soon	that	there	they	this
too	under	want	was	well
went	what	white	who	will
with	yes			

Publishing Consulting

Public Service Projects

Author Visits

Follow us on Social Media

Class Sets and Wholesale Books

Read Alouds

Gift Sets & Book Boxes

Contact Information

- NowIAmNia@gmail.com
- www.NowIAmNia.org
- @NowIAmNia
- @NowIAmNiaBooks
- @Red_Panda_Artz
- 207-613-6887

The Author & Illustrator of "Nia Means Purpose"

Send Us Photos of you reading for a chance to win prizes.

Certificate of Completion

This certificate is awarded to

_____

For

Completing ALL of the activities in the P is for PURPOSE Activity Book!

This certifies that

You are a letters, numbers, shapes, and colors recognizing STAR!

The Now I Am Nia Foundation, Inc.

Nia means purpose.
www.NowIAmNia.org

_____
Date

Made in the USA
Middletown, DE
14 May 2022